Beautiful KILLER

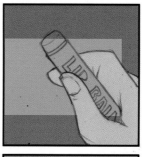
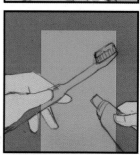

FLIGHT VA2160 DATE 10APR

ORIGIN
LONDON

DESTINATION
TOKYO

OPERATED BY VIRGIN ATLANTIC AIRWAYS

Introduction By
GAREB SHAMUS

I knew this project was going to be a hit the minute Jimmy told me about it, and this only got better from there.

I've always liked the idea of strong female leads in comic books, but experience has shown that's it's a difficult idea to put into practice. Luckily for us, Jimmy had a great story to tell. We then enlisted the extremely talented Adam Hughes for all our lead female character designs. And really, who else could you possibly want? He really hit the mark - she was strong, sexy and, of course, struck the right pose with a gun.

Unfortunately, Hughes wasn't available to illustrate the interiors, but Jimmy came through for us again. He had an artist who he knew was the *only* man for the job: Phil Noto. Boy was he right. He had the perfect style for this story, and his work is simply stunning. He's also a bit of a renaissance man: penciler, inker and colorist all rolled into one.

I couldn't wait to start seeing the finished pages, which took a little longer than expected. Phil had a full-time job, so he was working on *Beautiful Killer* after hours. Phil would also hand in practically the whole issue at one time instead of sending in pages as he went along. He wanted to make sure the whole book remained consistent in style and quality throughout, instead of being a collection of individual pages. And let me tell you, all that extra time and effort more than paid off!

What you now hold in your hands is the culmination of 12 months of hard work by Jimmy, Phil and the entire Black Bull crew. I couldn't have asked for a better finished product. I just wish there was more of it...and keep your fingers crossed, because maybe one day there will.

See ya!

Gareb Shamus

I had so much confidence just two days ago.

48 hours later and I'm a mess.

If I can only stop shaking...

...just long enough to take the shot.

I spent nineteen years of my life on an island with two of the most loving people on earth. Now I find myself forcibly abandoned in an environment of hostility and bitterness.

Some of this is my fault, I have to admit. I chose to take this a step further, follow it through till the end...

My parents have been warning me about this, protecting me as best they could since I was an infant.

I simply have no choice. It's either them or me, and after what they did to my parents... my life... it's going to be them.

I intercepted a string of cellphone calls that led me to this moment. I am sure on any other day, it would be impossible not to fall in love with this city...the architecture... the history, its people... any other day... but not today.

And not now.

Seven floors above the street I wait, for a light to come on, a man to enter a room and then... then what?

I planned this down to the last detail. I'm ready for anything or everything to go wrong... I got a plan "B" and "C", I got a quick out and I even have an alibi if need be, all set up and ready to go....

So why can't I stop shaking... why does every bone in my body want to get down from here, take the money my parents left me and head to the Virgin Islands and try to forget all that's happened?

I already know that answer, and to back it up, I have this... a photo of days gone by, but never forgotten...

For them, I have to be strong, have to balance the scales...

...for them I will endure.

KINGSLEY, SOMETIMES YOU CAN BE A REAL ASS...

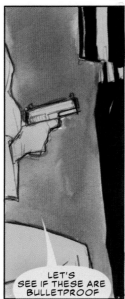

NOW...

Got to remember what Mom taught me... breathe normally... relax... exhale on the squeeze...

Focus on the job at hand, take a step out of your own head and make the weapon become an extension of yourself.

Turn on the laser scope and read out the type of glass.

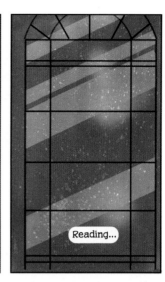

Reading...

Four inches thick, probably high-impact bullet proof glass. Got to make the ajustment, factor in density, projection and speed.

Movement inside... come on, turn on the light...

Bingo. If my calculations are correct...

... Axel Serod is going to have the headache of his life.

15

THIS IS PRETTY IMPRESSIVE STUFF...SEALS BOTH ENDS OF A DOOR AT ONCE. YOU CAN LITERALLY LOCK YOURSELF IN...

WHO CARES...I NEED TO...

YOU NEED TO RELAX AND GO TO A HOSPITAL. YOU ARE GOING TO NEED SOME PLASTIC SURGERY AND WE HAVE TO RUN AUDITORY TESTS. YOUR HEARING MAY BE PERMANENTLY DAMAGED.

YEAH, YEAH, WHATEVER. WILSON, GET OVER HERE...

THIS AREA HAS BEEN COMPROMISED. CALL IN A CREW TO CLEAN THIS PLACE. TELL THEM TO GRAB THE TAPES FROM THE FRONT OFFICE. I WANT TO KNOW WHO THIS GUY IS.

ACTUALLY, IT WAS A YOUNG GIRL, SIR...THEY SAW HER COME IN...

WHOEVER IT IS SEARCHED THE OFFICE AND VANISHED. IF SHE WANTED TO, I'D BE DEAD ALREADY. I NEED TIME TO CLEAR MY HEAD, BRING THE CAR UP FRONT.

WHERE TO, SIR? LOCAL HOSPITAL IS A FEW BLOCKS AWAY OR WE CAN HEAD INTO THE COMPANY COMPOUND AND LET HALLIDAY TAKE CARE OF YOUR EAR.

TOO RISKY. IF WE ARE BEING WATCHED, WE WOULD BE PLAYING RIGHT INTO THEIR HANDS. LET'S GO TO THE HOSPITAL. DROP ME OFF AND DRIVE AROUND THE CITY 'TIL YOU FEEL YOU'RE NOT BEING FOLLOWED, THEN REPORT BACK TO THE COMPANY.

WHO DO YOU THINK SHE IS WORKING FOR?

I'VE CROSSED SIDES SO OFTEN, IT WOULD BE EASIER TO FIGURE OUT WHO IT ISNT. WHAT IS PUZZLING ME MORE IS WHAT SHE IS LOOKING FOR...AND IF SHE FOUND IT.

WELL, WHOEVER SHE IS, SHE SURE DID A THOROUGH JOB. NOT ONLY WAS EVERY DOORWAY SEALED, BUT THE FRONT OFFICE DOWNSTAIRS SAID THAT THE POWER WAS CUT ON THE SECURITY ROOM. THERE ARE NO SURVEILLANCE TAPES OF HER.

GONNA FORM A FAN CLUB, WILSON?

NEXT BLOCK MAKE A RIGHT THEN ANOTHER QUICK RIGHT INTO THE ALLEY. DO IT NOW, OR I PAINT THE WINDSHIELD RED.

ANNA AND INGSLEY COLE. WHAT HAVE THEY GOT TO DO WITH THIS?

EVERYTHING...

EVERYTHING? THESE TWO WERE REMOVED FROM ACTIVE DUTY AS OF A COUPLE OF DAYS AGO...NOTHING LEFT OF THEM BUT TINY LITTLE CHUNKS...

SHUT UP!

WACK!

THE KID...YOU'RE THEIR KID. I DON'T KNOW IF YOU KNOW THIS OR NOT, BUT I'M THE PERSON WHO ALMOST PUT YOUR DAD SIX-FEET-UNDER YEARS AGO. WE WERE CLOSE FRIENDS BACK THEN. TOUGH BASTARD, THAT KINGSLEY...I'D SWEAR HE HAD NINE LIVES... UNFORTUNATELY FOR HIM, THEY RAN OUT.

WHACK!

THERE WASN'T ENOUGH LEFT OF HIM TO FILL AN ASHTRAY, AND YOUR MOM... WHAT A MESS. SHE WAS SO BEAUTIFUL...SHE HAD A GREAT CAREER AHEAD OF HER, AND SHE BLOWS IT ON THAT APPALLING SCIENCE PROJECT. NINETEEN YEARS GO BY. THEY DISAPPEAR, KEEP SUCH A LOW PROFILE NO ONE CAN FIND THEM AND THEN, WHEN THEY SURFACE... DEAD IN LESS THAN AN HOUR.

I DON'T KNOW IF YOU'RE AWARE OF THIS, BUT IF IT WEREN'T FOR TRACES OF YOUR DNA, WE WOULD NEVER HAVE KNOWN YOU EXISTED.

BUT WE DO... AND NOW YOU'RE BEING HUNTED. I FEEL BAD FOR YOU, GIRL...I GUESS I HAVE TO, BEING THAT I'M PRACTICALLY YOUR UNCLE...HELL, I MIGHT EVEN BE YOUR DADDY. YOUR MOM WAS SUCH A SLUT BACK THEN IT'S HARD TO BELIEVE...

19

23

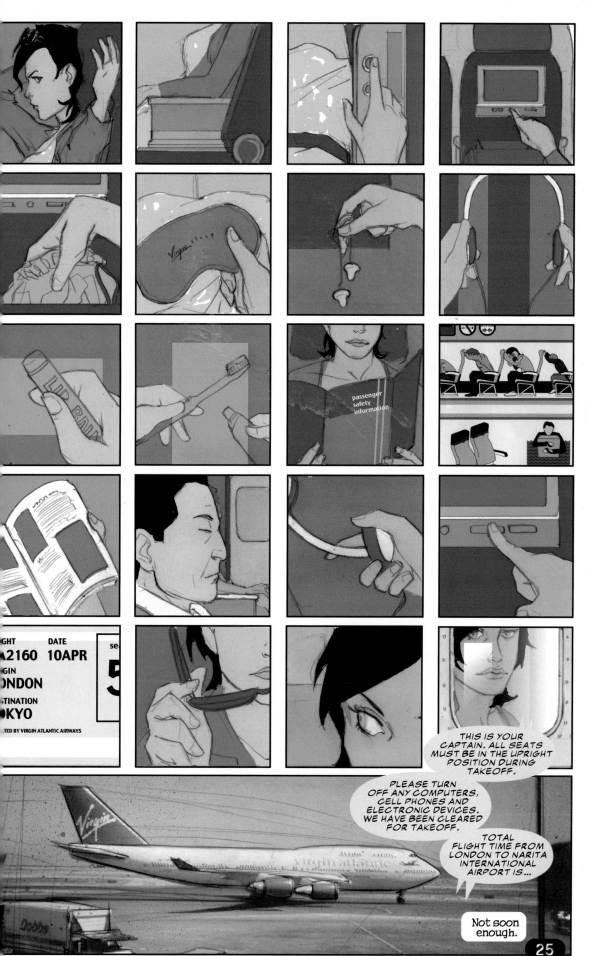

THIS IS YOUR CAPTAIN. ALL SEATS MUST BE IN THE UPRIGHT POSITION DURING TAKEOFF.

PLEASE TURN OFF ANY COMPUTERS, CELL PHONES AND ELECTRONIC DEVICES. WE HAVE BEEN CLEARED FOR TAKEOFF.

TOTAL FLIGHT TIME FROM LONDON TO NARITA INTERNATIONAL AIRPORT IS...

Not soon enough.

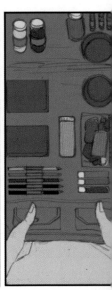

Three days ago, my parent's ex-partners ended their business relationship with a bang and left me an orphan.

24 hours ago, I tracked down one of the men responsible for this crime.

12 hours ago, I shot both his ears off and watched him die, but not before he led me to the person behind all this...

Now I'm flying across the world to face God-knows-what, and then try to get on with my life.

The plan is simple, right?

Track down someone that should already be dead, and finish the job once and for all.

I'm in way over my head. This, I know.

What I also know is what my mother taught me, years ago: how to change, become someone else...

How to hide in plain sight.

I miss my mother.

SEE, SWEETHEART, BECAUSE OF THE LACK OF PIGMENT IN YOUR SKIN, JUST APPLYING THE RIGHT COMBINATION OF COLOR CHANGES YOUR WHOLE APPEARANCE IN A MATTER OF MINUTES.

NEXT WE WORK ON THE EYELINERS.

MOTHER, WE'VE DONE THIS A ZILLION TIMES...YOU KEEP TELLING ME THIS IS IMPORTANT, BUT YOU NEVER TELL ME WHY.

HUSH, BRIGIT. JUST DO AS I SAY... AND TRUST ME.

Mom knew this all was going to happen.

She knew every day we had was a special day that could have been our last.

We were living on borrowed time and she never let on for a second.

They loved me so much they kept it a secret for as long as they could.

Everything changed that day.

ANNA...

BRING BRIGIT DOWN HERE.

IT'S TIME WE HAD OUR TALK.

And talk we did. Dad said he was going to start from the beginning, and he did.

He told me how he had been an agent for British Intelligence for two decades. How, because of his skills, he was forced to play both sides against the middle a number of times.

How this had something to do with why the three of us were here, cut off from the outside world, on a small island outside Venice, Italy.

Why we could never leave this place and why we could never relax for a second and think we were safe.

COURTNEY, MAKE SURE TO LET ME KNOW IF THERE ARE ANY CHANGES IN HIS CONDITION.

YES, MR. KELLY.

He told me all about an agent named Natassia K, whom he helped fake her own death, then defect from Russia and work for the Brits. He told me how she was later killed in action.

He told me how an agent named Axel Serod, working freelance for another party, jumped ship and almost killed him...all in the same day.

My mother told me that at that time, unbeknownst to her, Kingsley was fighting for his life only five doors away. She had no idea my father had been shot and retrieved and was, at that very moment, struggling to survive.

She was knee-deep in her work. The Criterion project was finally starting to make headway and, aside from a couple of unsettling drawbacks, the tests were showing some positive results in the lab rats they tested.

THE 2% BOOST IN ADRENALINE HAS HELPED SPEED UP TISSUE RESTORATION 30% FASTER.

THE REBUILT MUSCLE STRENGTH IS SHOWING BETTER STAMINA RESULTS AS WELL.

IF WE CAN REDUCE THE SIDE EFFECTS AND CONTAIN AND ADVANCE THE FLOW OF CELL RENEWAL, NOT ONLY CAN WE REPLACE TORN MUSCLE TISSUE AND STRENGTHEN IT, BUT WE COULD ALSO ONE DAY SLOW DOWN THE AGING PROCESS BY ADVANCING PRODUCTION OF NERVE AND BRAIN CELLS TO OVERCOME THE CONSTANT REDUCTION OF EXPIRED CELLS.

Mr. Kelly had ordered us to prepare a couple of vials of this experimental drug.

Remember, we haven't perfected it by a long shot... the most success we've had was on lab rats and a dog with a torn ligament.

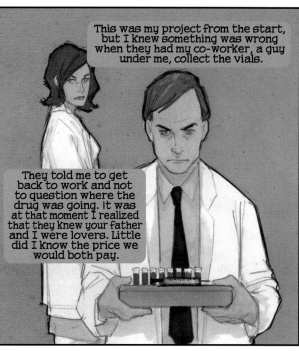

This was my project from the start, but I knew something was wrong when they had my co-worker, a guy under me, collect the vials.

They told me to get back to work and not to question where the drug was going. It was at that moment I realized that they knew your father and I were lovers. Little did I know the price we would both pay.

Your mother knew nothing. You have to understand, Brigit, your father was the oldest agent still in the field at the time. This was a job where youth was a prerequisite.

When I was shot, I was already on the top of the expendable list.

I was the first human guinea pig for them, and by God, they were going to use me.

Your father is right, sweetheart. They were waiting for an opportunity to try the drug on a human for months, but there was still so much we didn't know about it at the time...to make matters worse, Kelly wouldn't tell me a thing.

Not where the drug was being taken and on whom it was being used.

I was pissed...and starting to get a really bad feeling inside.

Mr. Kelly told me to get back to work and that I would be briefed on everything...

Eventually.

What could I do? He was my boss... and in those days, any form of inquiry was considered an act of insurrection and would be answered with some form of discipline. They were running a tight ship.

I complied and went back to work.

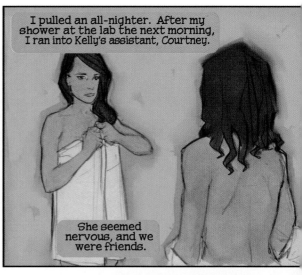

I pulled an all-nighter. After my shower at the lab the next morning, I ran into Kelly's assistant, Courtney.

She seemed nervous, and we were friends.

We were the only two agents around, so I asked her where the serum went.

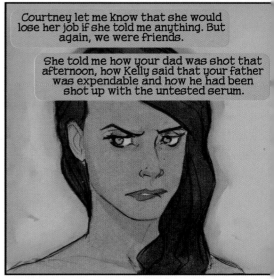

Courtney let me know that she would lose her job if she told me anything. But again, we were friends.

She told me how your dad was shot that afternoon, how Kelly said that your father was expendable and how he had been shot up with the untested serum.

I freaked.

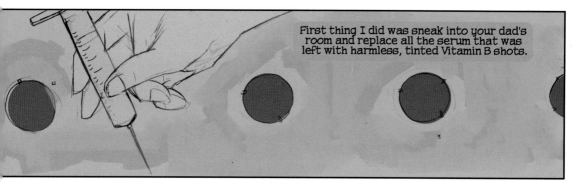

First thing I did was sneak into your dad's room and replace all the serum that was left with harmless, tinted Vitamin B shots.

During my lunch break I emptied out all of my accounts. Retirement accounts, off shore accounts, everything. I held on to half and forwarded the rest to a friend in Italy.

Everything was untraceable.

I packed only what I couldn't replace. Family photos, some handed-down heirlooms and my research discs.

Oh...and my gun.

I snuck in to see your father later that day. His condition was better, but he was still in for the ride of his life. This much I knew.

Brigit, darling...I loved your father... and in order to save his life I had to say goodbye to everything I had worked my whole life for.

In my heart, I knew if he stayed there, they would have eventually killed him. Without him my life had no meaning.

I did what I had to do to get your father out of there. I was taught by the best.

I had a plan and I had to make it happen fast.

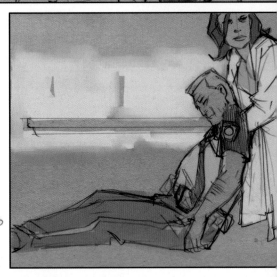

We did what we could and never looked back.

THERE WAS A TIME KINGSLEY COLE AND I WERE LOVERS, DID YOU KNOW THAT?

WHAT MAKES YOU THINK I WANT TO HEAR ABOUT THAT? THAT'S GROSS.

IT WAS A LONG TIME AGO AND FAR, FAR AWAY. IF IT WEREN'T FOR HIS HELP, I WOULDN'T BE WHERE I AM TODAY.

YOU HAVE SOME WAY OF SHOWING YOUR THANKS.

HUSH, LITTLE GIRL. THERE IS SO MUCH YOU STILL NEED TO LEARN...

SAVE IT FOR ANOTHER DAY. WE GOT CONFIRMATION ON THE COLE GIRL. SHE IS HEADING IN ON FLIGHT 2160 FROM LONDON. IT WILL BE LANDING IN 45 MINUTES. MY GUESS IS THAT SHE HAS SOME UNFINISHED BUSINESS HERE.

Your mother and I had to move quickly. When we left the agency there was no turning back.

We knew every caseworker was going to get a call that same day, and as far as we knew, we had limited time to act.

FLIGHT CREW PREPARE FOR LANDING.

Your mother had an old friend that owed her big time, and he was warned that we would be heading his way. We got into Italy and met up with him there.

WE WILL BE ARRIVING AT NARITA INTERNATIONAL IN 25 MINUTES.

YOU'RE TALKING ABOUT UNCLE DOLPHIN?

YEAH, ALADINO DELFINI. YOUR MOTHER SAVED HIS FAMILY'S LIFE YEARS AGO. WE NEVER WOULD HAVE SURVIVED WITHOUT THEIR HELP.

IT HAPPENS LIKE THAT SOMETIMES.

WE HAVEN'T SEEN HIM FOR A WHILE.

I KNOW THAT, DADDY; YOU'VE EXPLAINED IT BEFORE. I STILL DON'T LIKE IT.

NOR SHOULD WE. REMEMBER WHAT I SPOKE ABOUT...THE PEOPLE WHO WOULD WANT US DEAD?

YES. I REMEMBER.

BECAUSE I AM... DIFFERENT.

WELL, THAT AND THE FACT THAT YOUR MOTHER AND I HAVE INFORMATION THAT THEY WANT. IT'S A BAD SCENE EITHER WAY, BRIGIT...

TELL ME ABOUT THE ISLAND AGAIN...ABOUT HOW WE CAME TO BE A FAMILY.

Your mother and I purchased the island from Uncle Dolphin and bought a boat to get to it. Our trail was cold as ice. To send the agency off our trail even more, we paid a young couple we know to use our credit cards a couple of times overseas, then destroy them.

Months later, your mother was pregnant with you and I started having some inner ear problems. Dizziness and nausea were something your mom and I had in common every morning. At least her problems were natural. Mine were side effects from my "cure" that never left my side.

When you were born, the world suddenly became a brilliant place again, full of possibilities and promise.

Granted, we didn't know what side effects the Criterion serum would have on you, but so far, most have been positive.

For someone with such fair skin, you had no ill reactions to sunlight. There's a subtle pigment in your skin, but by all appearances, it's stark white.

The other things that we noticed were your pupils and the obvious differences in each eye. Again, another plus because of your amplified night vision.

It seemed your ability to learn and the rate you absorbed information was incredible. We still don't know if that is because of the chemical cocktail or just the lack of TV in your life.

Because of all this, we had to push your learning even harder and faster...and take it to a darker place.

ONE DAY WE WILL BE DISCOVERED AND ALL WE HAVE...ALL WE HAVE KNOWN, WILL END, AND YOU WILL HAVE TO MAKE A LIFE FOR YOURSELF...WITHOUT US.

HONEY, I HATE TO PUT IT TO YOU THIS WAY, BUT WHEN OUR LIFE CATCHES BACK UP TO US, YOU WILL HAVE TO PUT EVERYTHING WE EVER TAUGHT YOU TO USE... FOR REAL.

NO PLAYING, NO PRACTICE... REAL WORLD STUFF. YOU'RE GOING TO HAVE TO DISAPPEAR AND NEVER LOOK BACK.

I KNOW.

I JUST WANT TO MAKE SURE I AM READY FOR THE THINGS YOU GUYS COULDN'T TEACH ME ABOUT...

SUCH AS?

WELL... LIVING ALONE AND...

BOYS!

KINGSLEY... ABOUT ALADINO... WHAT DO YOU...

RELAX...I'M SURE WE WILL HEAR FROM HIM. MAYBE SOMETHING HAPPENED AT HOME. THIS HAS HAPPENED BEFORE.

DON'T WORRY, EVERYTHING IN GOOD TIME.

TIME...

"I FEEL LIKE IT'S BEGINNING TO RUN OUT."

43

NOT A BAD DISGUISE. MY GIRLS RADIOED FROM INSIDE WHAT YOU LOOK LIKE, NOW GET IN THE CAR.

WELL, IF IT ISN'T NATASSIA K, COMING ALL THE WAY OUT TO GREET ME PERSONALLY. LOOKS LIKE YOU SAVED ME THE TRIP OF KILLING YOU ELSEWHERE.

HOW DO YOU KNOW ME?

MY FATHER IS...WAS PRETTY THOROUGH WITH HIS FILES.

YOU DON'T LOOK LIKE YOU AGED MUCH IN 20 YEARS. YOU MUST TELL ME YOUR SECRET BEFORE I KILL YOU.

'FRAID NOT, SWEETCHEEKS!

ZXXXXXXX!

I GOT TO ADMIT, THIS IS ONE COCKY GIRL.

I AM NOT AS IMPRESSED. IF SHE IS THE DAUGHTER OF THOSE TWO, SHE IS MORE DANGEROUS THAN SHE LOOKS. PUT HER IN THE TRUNK.

WE ARE CLEAR.

GOOD.

EVERYONE IN THEN.

BRIGIT, NO ONE LIVING KNOWS YOU EXIST YET AND WE PLAN TO KEEP IT THAT WAY.

LISTEN TO ME CAREFULLY... WE'VE REHEARSED THIS DOZENS OF TIMES.

ANNA, UPDATE ME ON THE STATUS OF THE ISLAND. WHAT ARE WE UP AGAINST?

IT LOOKS LIKE KELLY, SEROD AND A FEW DOZEN OTHERS.

COUPLE BOATS COMING IN FROM THE WEST ALSO.

LOOKS LIKE TWO CHOPPERS AS WELL.

KINGSLEY, WE'VE GOT TO GET HER OUT OF HERE NOW!

BRIGIT, SWEETHEART, LET'S GET GOING...

DAD, I DON'T WANT TO GO... BETWEEN THE THREE OF US MAYBE THERE IS A CHANCE...

THEY ARE NOT GOING TO STOP UNTIL WE ARE DEAD. AS LONG AS THEY DON'T KNOW YOU EXIST, YOU'RE GOING TO BE SAFE. I WISH THERE WERE ANOTHER WAY, BUT THERE ISN'T.

LET'S GET YOU GEARED UP.

FORGET THE INITIAL PLAN TO FIND UNCLE DOLPHIN ONCE YOU REACH THE COAST. I'M GUESSING THEY GOT TO ALADINO AND FORCED OUR LOCATION OUT OF HIM, THAT'S WHY WE HAVEN'T HEARD FROM HIM IN WEEKS.

DAMNIT, I KNOW HE WOULDN'T HAVE GIVEN US UP WITHOUT A FIGHT! MY GUESS IS HE'S LONG GONE.

BRIGIT, IT'S GOING TO HAVE TO BE PLAN "B" FROM HERE ON IN.

YOU HAVE THE PACK WITH ENOUGH MONEY, CONTACT INFORMATION, LAPTOP WITH MAPS, YOUR MOTHER'S WORK FILES, PASSPORTS WITH YOUR NEW NAME AND SO ON. GET TO THE CITY AND KEEP MOVING. DON'T STOP, DON'T LOOK BACK... AND MOST IMPORTANT: TRUST NO ONE.

OH, MY PRECIOUS GIRL, REMEMBER WHAT YOUR FATHER SAID.

YOU HAVE TO START A NEW LIFE AND KEEP THIS ONE IN THE PAST. FORGET WHAT'S GOING TO HAPPEN TODAY. YOUR MOTHER AND I HAVE A SCORE TO SETTLE AND THANK GOD WE HAVE HAD THIS MUCH PRECIOUS TIME TOGETHER. YOU GO LIVE YOUR LIFE AND SEE THE WORLD BUT YOU MUST REMEMBER ONE THING... YOU MUST NEVER TRY TO SEEK REVENGE FOR THIS. THE MINUTE YOU COME UP ON THE AGENCY'S RADAR, YOU ARE GOOD AS DEAD.

YOUR FATHER IS RIGHT. WE MADE OUR OWN CHOICES IN OUR LIFE AND NOW THEY HAVE CAUGHT UP TO US. THERE IS NO REASON YOU HAVE TO PAY FOR OUR SINS.

GO, SWEETHEART, SEE THE WORLD, FALL IN LOVE, START YOUR OWN FAMILY, AND NEVER FORGET...YOUR PARENTS LOVE YOU MORE THAN LIFE ITSELF AND ARE PROUD OF YOU.

I CANT DO THIS ALONE, ≷SNIFF≷ PLEASE...

PLEASE COME WITH ME.

51

MOM... DAD...

...GOODBYE.

NOW...

KOFF! KOFF! KOFF!

WHAT THE...

GAAKKKKK!

54

The airport... was talking to Nastassia and next thing I know I was getting cattle prodded and shoved into a trunk.

That's not all I remember.

I was shot... point blank. Three times.

I'm still alive.

Feel sick as a dog, already threw up twice.

Okay, so I'm still alive and the bullets didn't kill me... so what do I do now?

I have to assume I'm in the trunk of Nastassia's car and they think I'm probably dead. My advantage.

What would Dad do?

Probably would never have gotten himself into such a stupid spot. What was I thinking confronting Nastassia in broad daylight?

Stupid, stupid, stupid.

MOM...

HOW THE HELL IS SHE...?

MOM, I CAN'T SEE ANYTHING...

I AM RIGHT HERE, BABY-- I'LL GO GET US SOME HELP.

MOM, HUH?

NORMALLY THIS WOULD BE A VERY TOUCHING SCENE. BUT IN LIGHT OF THE LAST FEW WEEKS, I COULDN'T THINK OF A BETTER WAY TO MAKE YOU SUFFER THAN TO MAKE YOU WATCH YOUR OWN DAUGHTER DIE SLOWLY.

59

FINE...WHAT IS IT YOU WANT TO KNOW?

Basically, I wanted to know everything, and that's what I asked her. One question at a time.

She told me how my father had helped her fake her death a couple of times, that this was used to flush out bad agents.

She explained how Mr. Kelly had taken my mother's work after she had disappeared and had reworked her formula a tiny bit 'til it was worth more than anyone had ever imagined. The tissue restoration was just the beginning.

The Criterion project took on another life and big business eventually shut down the corporation when the spy game began to lose more money than it was making. Medical technology became the main source of income... and she and the other remaining members left, taking Criterion with them, and formed a new company.

Meditek became the new home for Nastassia, Axel Serod and Mr. Kelly, as well as a number of scientists that had been working both sides for a number of years. They were becoming millionaires the legitimate way.

Other than a piece of wet work here and there, she had explained that she and Axel had become the company's lion tamers. Their job was to deal with former agents that were considered threats to their business.

My parents were on the top 10 list.

WHY CHASE DOWN MY PARENTS?

YOU KNEW THEY WERE NEVER GOING TO COME OUT OF HIDING, WHY NOT JUST LEAVE THEM ALONE?

WE COULDN'T. NO MATTER HOW SUCCESSFUL WE WERE BECOMING, WE KNEW IT... UGGGHH... IT WOULD ALL FALL APART IF YOUR PARENTS DECIDED TO COME OUT OF HIDING. WE HAD NO CLUE THEY HAD A CHILD OR SOMETHING TO PROTECT. THEY JUST UP AND LEFT ONE DAY AND TOOK HALF THE BUILDING WITH THEM.

UHHHGH... THEY HAD TO BE ELIMINATED, DON'T YOU UNDERSTAND? EVERYTHING WE HAD WAS INVESTED IN YOUR MOTHER'S RESEARCH...

SO IMPORTANT THAT PEOPLE HAD TO DIE FOR IT?

PEOPLE THAT WERE YOUR FRIENDS? MY FATHER TOLD ME THAT HE HAD SAVED YOUR LIFE A NUMBER OF TIMES...

IS THAT HOW YOU SHOW YOUR LOYALTY?

¿KOFF¿...YES. YOUR PARENTS KNEW THE RISKS WHEN THEY LEFT. DON'T BE SO NAIVE.

THIS WAS BIGGER THAN ALL OF US. I'M GUESSING IT'S PART OF THE REASON THAT YOU TOOK THREE BULLETS POINT BLANK AND ARE STILL BREATHING.

YEAH, AND I'M GUESSING THAT IT'S ALSO WHY YOU LOOK ONLY THIRTY AND HAVE TWO GROWN DAUGHTERS.

LISTEN, I NEED TO KNOW WHO GAVE THE ORDERS TO HAVE MY PARENTS KILLED. I WANT TO KNOW HOW I CAN FINALLY END ALL THIS AND GET ON WITH MY OWN LIFE.

TELL ME.

YOUR PARENTS DID A GOOD JOB ON *THAT* MAN ON THE ISLAND. THAT WAS MR. KELLY. YOU GREASED AXEL IN PARIS AND ¿KOFF¿ I'M LAST ON THE LIST.

REALLY? I PERSONALLY DOUBT THE CHAIN ENDS HERE, BUT I WILL INVESTIGATE THAT MYSELF.

MY FATHER DID TELL ME YOU WERE THE ONE TO WATCH OUT FOR, BUT YOU DON'T LOOK LIKE MUCH TO ME NOW.

LIKE YOU SAVED MY MOM AND DAD?

YOU STUPID GIRL! DON'T YOU UNDERSTAND? THIS IS IT! GET ON WITH YOUR PITIFUL LIFE, JUST SAVE MY DAUGHTER...¿KOFF¿.

2 DAYS LATER.

The funny thing about killing Nastassia is that instead of feeling good about it, I felt more detached from everything. Actually, surprisingly sad. It was as though I was on autopilot for the last week. No time to think...just time to act.

Of course I called an ambulance for Kimi, I had a lot in common with her in more ways than one. She too was a product of her environment. No reason for her to pay for her mother's sins so dearly. Trixie on the other hand... well, nobody's perfect.

These last two days spent investigating Meditek has cooled me down to the point where I'm starting to question if this is still a good idea to see through.

I also am beginning to realize that I may have taken on more than I can handle, mysterious healing power or not...I'm only one person.

Yeah... the one person that has to finish what I started.

Confidence, girl... remember your training. Breathe deep.

Here we are, Meditek's main office building. No turning back now. The last person for me to deal with at the end of this yellow brick road is now sitting high and mighty in the penthouse.

I sure hope he is enjoying his last day on Earth.

TWIPP

FTTT!

DING!

WHAT?

HEY, BOYS!

FTTT!

FTTT!

WELCOME, MS. COLE. PLEASE COME INSIDE, WE HAVE MUCH TO DISCUSS.

I AM NOT SAYING A WORD UNTIL YOU TELL YOUR GOONS TO LEAVE THE ROOM. THIS IS BETWEEN US.

REALLY? IF YOU PUT DOWN YOUR GUN, I PROMISE NO HARM WILL COME TO YOU. WE WILL JUST TALK.

SORRY, NO CAN DO. CLEAR THE ROOM, I KEEP MY GUN AND WE TALK. YOU HAVE MY WORD THAT I WON'T SHOOT YOU.

HA! FINE...EVERYONE OUT, BUT REMEMBER, STAY CLOSE. JUST FOR INSURANCE, MS. COLE, I AM GOING TO KEEP THIS CONTROLLER IN MY HAND. IF I PRESS THIS BUTTON, THEY WILL BE BACK IN HERE WITH GUNS BLAZING IN LESS THAN A SECOND, UNDERSTOOD?

FAIR ENOUGH.

YOU MUST UNDERSTAND WHY I AM HERE.

I WANT TO SAY UP FRONT THAT, AS FAR AS I AM CONCERNED, ALL THE BUSINESS YOU HAD WITH MY PARTNERS AND SISTERS IS OVER. THEY TOLD ME THAT IF YOU DIDN'T CALL AN AMBULANCE FOR MY SISTER KIMI, SHE WOULD BE DEAD. I THANK YOU FOR THAT.

MY MOTHER, ON THE OTHER HAND, DESERVED WHAT SHE HAD COMING TO HER, AS DID AXEL... MY STEPFATHER.

MOTHER?

WELL...SORRY. NOT THAT KNOWING THIS WOULD HAVE MADE ANY DIFFERENCE.

I UNDERSTAND. I ASKED MY FAMILY AND CO-WORKERS TO LEAVE ALL THIS BUSINESS BEHIND A LONG TIME AGO, BUT THEY PERSISTED, AGAINST MY WISHES.

WELL, HERE WE ARE NOW. SO PLEASE LET ME KNOW, WHAT IS OUR NEXT STEP?

WHAT HAPPENED TO CRITERION? BIOLOGICAL WEAPONS?

NOTHING SO EVIL I AM AFRAID. THERE IS LIMITED PROFIT AND JAIL TIME INVOLVED IN THAT BUSINESS. YOUR MOTHER'S WORK INDIRECTLY CREATED A DRUG THAT NOT ONLY SLOWED DOWN THE AGING PROCESS, BUT ONCE DEVELOPED AND RE-WORKED, HAS THE POWER TO REDUCE AND EVENTUALLY KILL THE PRODUCTION OF MOST MAJOR CANCER CELL GROWTH IN THE BODY.

MORE VALUABLE THAN ANY WEAPON, WE HAD THE GOLDEN GOOSE IN THE MEDICAL WORLD.

THEN WHERE IS THIS DRUG BEING USED? I NEVER HEARD OF IT.

WELL, WE HAVE INTERESTS IN OTHER PHARMACEUTICALS WE PRODUCED, AS WELL AS STOCK, WHICH WE PAID FOR. THOSE DRUGS HAVE YET TO BE USED.

WHEN WE PHASE OUT OUR OLD DRUGS, WE INTRODUCE NEW, STRONGER ONES. EVENTUALLY WE WILL GET TO THE FINAL ONE, BUT UNTIL THEN, THERE ARE BILLIONS TO BE HAD.

UNTIL THEN PEOPLE SUFFER AND DIE?

THAT'S OKAY WITH YOU?

DON'T YOU UNDERSTAND THAT BY NOT PREVENTING THESE DEATHS, YOU IN A WAY ARE RESPONSIBLE FOR THEM?

IS THERE A REALITY SWITCH ON YOU SOMEWHERE? WE INTRODUCE THIS DRUG RIGHT AWAY AND WE LOSE BILLIONS AND WE HAVE A POPULATION EXPLOSION ON OUR HANDS. IN CASE YOU DIDN'T NOTICE, THERE ISN'T ANYWHERE LEFT ON THIS PLANET WHERE ONE COULD BE LEFT ALONE... SPEAKING OF THAT, I HAVE AN OFFER FOR YOU.

ALL THIS VIOLENCE AND DEATH CAN END NOW. BY THE DOOR IS A CASE WITH ENOUGH MONEY FOR THREE LIFETIMES. TAKE IT AND GO. WE WILL NEVER SEE EACH OTHER AGAIN.

YOU HAVE TO UNDERSTAND, YOUR ONLY OTHER CHOICE, REALLY, IS TO BE KILLED RIGHT NOW. TRUST ME, THERE IS NO WAY OUT OF HERE ALIVE.

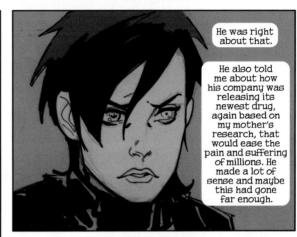

He was right about that.

He also told me about how his company was releasing its newest drug, again based on my mother's research, that would ease the pain and suffering of millions. He made a lot of sense and maybe this had gone far enough.

The deal was let him continue with his business and I could walk.

We shook on it.

BRIGIT COLE, YOU NO LONGER EXIST, NOW GO ON AND LIVE YOUR LIFE. YOU HAVE MY WORD THAT NO HARM WILL COME TO YOU.

His word.

Funny thing is, Tadashi, I do exist.

Your mother knew it, your father knew it.

And now your partners know it.

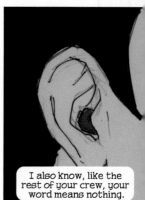

I also know, like the rest of your crew, your word means nothing.

...DON'T CARE WHAT I SAID, GET EVERYONE ON THIS. I NEED TO KNOW EVERYONE SHE COMES IN CONTACT WITH.

I WANT PHONE TAPS, PICTURES, THE WHOLE WORKS.

WHEN I'M SATISFIED THAT WE TRACKED DOWN EVERYONE SHE HAS EVER COME IN CONTACT WITH AND TERMINATED THEM...

...I WANT HER DEAD!

STUPID, STUPID, STUPID.

CLICK

FA-KOOM!

I spent 19 years of my life on an island with two of the most loving people on Earth. Now I find myself forcibly abandoned in an environment of hostility and bitterness.

Some of this is my fault, I admit. I chose to take this a step further, follow it through to the end...

My parents have been warning me about this, protecting me as best they could since I was an infant.

I simply have no choice. It's either them or me, and after what they did to my parents...my life...it's going to be them.

And now all I have to look forward to is only the rest of my life.

END.

Cover to *Beautiful Killer #2*
by Joe Jusko

GOD! LOOK AT THIS FIRM, TIGHT BOD,

I MUST BE A COMIC BOOK CHARACTER!!!...

BIG, BAGGY JEANS HELPS 'SELL' HER AS A 19-YEAR OLD

AH!

LONG NECK

BIGGISH EARS

DAVID BOWIE EYES

HAIR IS ORANGE W/ BLACK TIPS!

CUTE LITTLE CHIN

CENSORED

BOTTOM LIP IS SMALL + PUCKISH

THE BEST TEEN LOOK IS ACCOMPLISHED BY THE "BODY OF A WOMAN/FACE OF A LITTLE GIRL" TRICK

AH!

BEST WAYS TO "DESCRIBE"

1. CUT DOWN ON EXTRANEOUS FACIAL FEATURES
2. THINK "OVER-EXPOSED!"
3. DARK EYEBROWS, MASCARA AND LIPSTICK

TO GIVE HER THE LEAN CUT LOOK —
1. SMALL HIPS, VERY FEW CURVES (THINK TEEN BOY W/ BOOBS)
2. WIRY ARMS WITH ROUND SHOULDERS
3. GIVE HER HIGH-PLACED, FIRM, "I HATE HER" TEEN BOOBS!

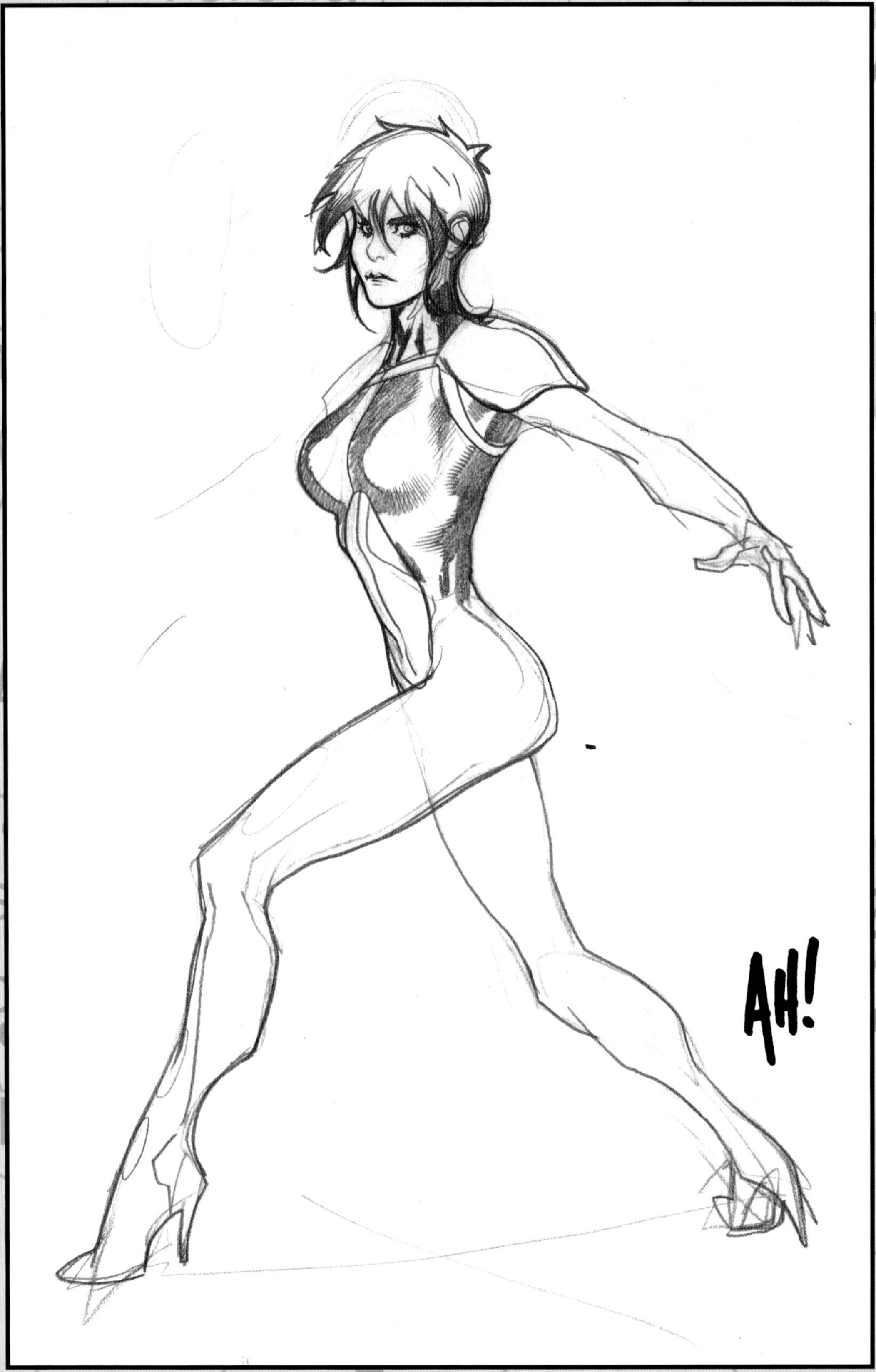
AH!

PHIL NOTO
SPOTLIGHT

noto

Take a look at these personal creations from Phil Noto. And of course, we all know who the guy on the right is.